*A la recherche
du temps perdu*

CRAIG RAINE

A la recherche
du temps perdu

PICADOR

First published 2000 by Picador
an imprint of Macmillan Publishers Ltd
25 Eccleston Place, London SW1W 9NF
Basingstoke and Oxford
Associated companies throughout the world
www.macmillan.co.uk

ISBN 0 330 37576 8

This poem was previously published in
Areté: the Arts Tri-Quarterly, Winter 1999.

9 8 7 6 5 4 3 2 1

A CIP catalogue record for this book is available from
the British Library.

Typeset by SetSystems Ltd, Saffron Walden, Essex
Printed and bound in Great Britain by
Mackays of Chatham plc, Chatham, Kent

'like a thing that falls through water,
she passes away'

Oscar Wilde, 'The Critic as Artist'

A la recherche du temps perdu

So I turn to a dead language again:
ineo, I go into, enter, begin.

Doleo, I am in pain, I grieve.
And everyone thinks I am being brave.

Ignis, ignis, masculine, fire:
at St Pancras Crematorium, I stare,

light-headed with caffeine,
at the light-oak coffin,

wondering what I feel, where I stand.
Vulnus, vulneris, neuter, a wound.

I watch the coffin vanish
to Mozart on tape, its varnish

about to come up in blisters
and burst into a boa

of full-length, rustling fire,
just as we reach the Dies Irae.

Sinews shrink from the flames.
Sinews shrink in the flames.

I sentimentalise
and then revise.

Iter, itineris, neuter, a journey.
Without end. Where the road is empty.

Sine plus ablative, without.
The words are in my mouth

but I can't teach myself
the simple, difficult lesson of grief.

Too terrible to learn. Too hard
to have the words by heart.

I can't accept you're dead.
You're still here, in my head:

irritating, prickly, unsalved,
unsolved, unlovable, loved.

That bubble at the corner of your mouth.
Which seems somehow to mean so much.

*   *   *   *

Sometimes unlovable.
Not always. And always beautiful.

Except for your beard,
which you hated, and I adored.

Which neither of us spoke about.
I was kept quiet

by your behaviour.
You behaved as if it wasn't there.

Whereas it was, one of the facts,
like the long guard hairs on a fox.

Twenty. Just under the chin. Peroxide
let them flourish in disguise.

Or you clipped them with fine scissors,
made in Germany, curvilinear,

kept at the back of a drawer –
hidden, but not hidden, like the hairs.

Almost oriental when they grew back:
tiny, shining, sparse, glint-black

like surgical stitches.
Tweezers raised unsightly blotches.

A student I taught Wyatt and Surrey
dropped his tweezers in my study,

a flinch of light in the carpet pile.
His nose was heartily male.

'They fle from me that sometyme did me tweke.'
Hypocrite, you laughed at my joke:

we never talked about any of this
until, after we split, electrolysis

also took permanent care
of all nine of your nipple hairs.

We were in bed together,
talking like sister and brother.

For once. Your black boy friend
objected to them, so that was the end.

I said, the guy's got to be mad.
Those things were a turn-on, I said.

And they were.
Your long glowing nipples shabby with hairs.

Big tits, you laughed. *Men love melons.*
Size. They might as well be melons,

for all the pleasure I feel.
They do nothing for me at all.

What has all this to do with anyone else?
Why all these intimate details?

You introduced me to Conrad's fiction.
The Nigger and its introduction

which says the writer makes things real.
His task: 'to make you hear, to make you feel –

it is, before all, to make you *see*.'
To make you *see*. Before all. I agree.

'That – and no more, and it is everything.'
Details that make you cringe

will make the reader *see*,
see the self you showed to me.

The vulgar fraction and the better half.
Shaving your legs in the bath

like Rembrandt, in a shower cap.
The razor's satin stripe through soap

like sap. Your shaven legs
sleek and sexual as stripped twigs.

You putting in a contact lens,
taking a new moon out of the cleanser,

meniscus at your fingertip.
You prise open the eyelid

and bend your head,
touch the eye as if it were hot,

a single dab, once,
like a wince

away from something dark,
shielding your face from shock.

Like someone warding off fate,
just a second too late.

Blink-blinking away the tears,
you could *see*. Were one of the seers.

(Turning aside
from AIDS . . .)

*   *   *   *

Tea. In your kitchen at Gillespie Road.
We talked about AIDS,

just after the genital herpes scare.
What, 1982, '83? There or round about there.

You were stanching a cold with a Kleenex
you plucked from its box

like a conjuror.
It became damper and smaller,

barely visible up your sleeve.
The size of a semibreve.

You almost made it disappear.
But not quite. It was still there.

Light-hearted, fatalistic,
you made light of it:

Well, you grinned, *I've fucked everyone.*
And you sipped your lapsang souchong.

(The odd white prole,
but black boys on the whole.

For preference a pick-up on the tube.
Tea the invariable prelude –

to calm their nerves – and talk.
Talk till they could believe their luck.)

Glenn Gould, then, singing along
to the 'Goldberg' Variations

in the sitting room, up the stairs
pairs and pairs and pairs

of handworked, high-heeled cowboy boots
(none, you said, the ideal style or fit)

and the photograph of you nude,
silver gelatin mounted on rag board,

on the bedroom wall,
showing nothing at all.

Nothing at all because
you are hugging your knees,

teeth wet, mouth wide,
thrown back hair and head.

Not quite *Vogue*, but beautiful.
You wanted to model

after you chucked your lecturing job.
You thought you'd give it a stab

and get together a photo-file.
You hired a professional

who fucked you on the studio bed
after he'd taken his shots of you naked.

In fact,
it wasn't a fuck.

It was a quick
suck.

Thirty seconds max.
He was really after a sandwich

with you and his girlfriend.
Which wasn't what you had in mind.

What happened, happened.
Were you innocent?

Surprised by all that juice and joy?
Or on the look out for a guy

where context might speed things up?
Snow White? Or Snow White drinking 7 Up?

It was your first adventure
with a total stranger.

And that was your modelling career.
Nothing else came of the idea,

except one solitary job for the *BMJ*:
Cystitis: Before and After. Relief Today.

All this, all this is why
no one saw me cry

the morning of your funeral.
My head was full

of grief and dates and calculations.
You'd chosen quotations

from Holub and Ruskin
but I could hardly listen.

I was trying to decide
whether you could have given me AIDS.

And my mind was busy,
watching you write an essay,

stretched out on the floor,
right hand holding your Sheaffer,

left hand propping your chin
just off the floor of the coffin,

lips pulled apart at the corner,
inside out, a urethra,

disclosing a seed of saliva
like dull Russian silver.

*   *   *   *

Miss Mary Lascelles at Somerville,
giving you a tutorial –

May we lay your written work
on the hearth-rug, so to speak?

Strangely appropriate,
since that's where you always scribbled it.

*   *   *   *

In my study,
Torso of a Young Woman by Brancusi,

open on the book rest,
virginal, undressed, a paradox,

and behind,
tied with tartan twine,

a year of your letters from Strasbourg.
Chaste. Factual. An epistolary iceberg.

Trace-elements of you everywhere:
I used to own your *Petit Robert*,

your boxed set of *La Traviata*,
a reproduction of August Macke –

all spoils of the break
until you claimed them back.

And I still possess
a grey chiffon dress

like a wisp of smoke,
clinging, weak,

a wardrobe stranger
on its stolen Harrods hanger.

You taught me your taste
as if I had to pass a test.

I'd adopted student standards:
bookshelves of bricks and chipboard,

the copper alarm clock
with the ping-pong tick,

ten Picasso bullfight posters,
Nescafé, Morphy Richards toaster

with emerald fern design,
one piece of stripped pine . . .

I was a kind of Deist with a small *d*:
whatever was, was OK by me,

even the landlord's floral curtains.
You, though, were scathing and certain:

you had visiting cards
(which you ironised: 'I deferred

to my father's anachronistic notion
of student customs . . .')

cut glass, a cafetière,
Mexican rugs, Struwwelpeter hair,

ballet pumps with gathered soles.
You were bilingual,

had been taught Sidney (not Wyatt)
by 'the writer, Antonia Byatt',

and at a fire-balloon party
given by Francis Huxley,

the nephew of Aldous,
you spilled a dish of peanuts

on his parquet floor.
Beautiful. Just leave them there,

he said, and you were impressed.
I was jealous, depressed

and faintly rebellious for once.
I wouldn't concede an inch.

I'd stub a fag out on the floor
and say, *Beautiful. Just leave it there.*

It really pissed you off. Thirty years on,
I think I'm my own man

but I have two 8-day clocks
with barely audible ticks,

and *figures* round the face,
not Roman numerals or milled spaces,

a Swiza and an Angelus,
as if you'd made the purchase.

You also formed my sexual tastes
by certain physical traits –

the way your knees whispered together
like words of a feather –

by alterations to my 'technique'
so that it suited yourself.

You taught me sex
was conversation and not a speech.

I wrote poetry to impress you
and you're in my writing, too:

if a woman scratches her face
that's you leaving your trace,

or counts the hairs in her brush,
or parts the hair of her bush . . .

You're everywhere. So it isn't odd
if there are traces of you in my blood . . .

*   *   *   *

Listening to 'A Whiter Shade of Pale',
galley slaves of the bar football.

*   *   *   *

Tunis. The palm trees' structure
is file and feather duster.

The sea is sparking like sandpaper.
Arabic script, its ripple and flutter

stencilled on whitewash.
The main café: a line of hookahs

like a single letter
practising itself. On the river,

a Muslim oarsman rowing to Mecca.
You are in school. Your teacher

points to your grave 9-year-old face:
la seule étoile de la classe.

One boy ironically claps.
Wind works through the palm tops.

The edge of a tent
is waving to attract attention.

You showed me your passport once,
a schoolgirl facing the lens,

la seule étoile de la classe
who couldn't settle for less,

whose mouth is already sad.
You never forgot the accolade,

which turned into a reproach
as you waited for the approach

of distinction. Or failure
like Perkin Warbeck or Anastasia.

You'd write. You'd explore the Amazon.
Your father was the bastard son

of Battistini, the Italian baritone or bass.
At Cambridge, he brought *Ulysses*

back from Paris and earned two lines
in *Speak, Memory* – refined

to a pair of initials, P. M.
Meeting him was like meeting a statesman.

He didn't shake hands.
He was silent. He was grand.

You were the suppliant.
He gave you his pronate left hand.

Tunis. Rome. He'd lived abroad.
He pronounced 'billiards' *biyards*.

He was like de Gaulle
awaiting destiny's call,

when the moment for France was ripe.
He called me 'the gutter-snipe'

(years later: he'd forgotten my name)
and frightened the young Michael Frayn

who was keen on another daughter.
You took after your father,

but you were a literary snob,
exasperated by the successfully glib,

mainly our mutual friends,
the Martins, Julians and Ians,

whose books would always be shallow
unless they got round to Dante and Plato . . .

You translated Flaubert for Penguin.
La Tentation de Saint Antoine. Pure protein.

And you published a novel
which was 'ambitious' and unreadable.

Even to me, who thought
I might have a walk-on part.

I just couldn't finish it. I tried
again. And again. I should have lied.

You forgave me. There were precedents,
after all: DuCamp passing sentence

(*Burn it!*) on *La Tentation* in manuscript
and Flaubert surviving the verdict . . .

(Plus long ago I'd gagged at your drafts
of Flaubert's foie gras text.)

By then, you knew you had AIDS.
Jamie had died in the States,

your ex-, the black bisexual.
So, what *I* thought, was trivial,

especially three years after publication.
(You'd been in Rome: *found my vocation.*

Guess. A job as a grave digger.
How did that take so long to figure out?)

And you needed a literary executor.
But I was already spoken for,

a huge estate, so I refused.
The AIDS I guessed

and didn't guess.
Was your request a request?

Or a threat? Or a subtle plea?
I guess I didn't want to see.

*   *   *   *

A year later, we were in Fornello's
in Southampton Row:

I was having the chocolate sponge,
you were having a cold revenge.

1990: the last time I saw you.
A tin sun out in the blue.

I gave you my new book of essays
and asked you what you thought of my play.

Of '1953'? You shook your head a bit.
I think Racine a very, very, very great poet.

Over the starter of house ravioli,
we'd quarrelled over Misha Maisky.

It was Beethoven with Argerich.
I had a spare ticket

so you came along.
Because Maisky sang along

as he played,
there was a delayed

echo like a transatlantic call,
peripheral, only just audible.

Rueful, you shook your head.
As if the fuss were in my head.

You 'couldn't hear it' until
the very end of the interval,

when we met your pianist friend
who was going before the end

because, because, *because*
of Maisky's horrible humming noise.

Why did I bring it up? No idea.
Shit. Desperate to *praise* your ear,

I remembered from years before
The Vulcan Bulletins by Sam Gulliver.

Sam Gulliver was a pseudonym
for James Hamilton-Paterson.

How could a *poet*? . . . you said.
And you'd shaken your head.

Title and author:
what an aural obstacle course.

All the cadence
of pick-a-sticks.

He won the Whitbread First Novel Prize,
I said, for something else,

his second novel.
The ethics of that gave you no trouble.

All publishing was corrupt and nasty,
as I should know. I swallowed my pasta.

Outside, you thanked me for lunch,
laughed, and took the plunge.

You were all charm.
You had taken my arm

so it pressed
against your right breast.

Your eyes swam with warmth
as if you loved me more than anything on earth.

Your hair was going grey.
Let's not repeat today.

*Why don't you come
to Gillespie Road sometime?*

An invitation. An invitation
I still can't fathom.

Asexual? A threat? A subtle plea?
Would you have gone to bed with me?

1990. I never saw you again.
You never went up the Amazon.

*   *   *   *

A la recherche du temps perdu.
Your favourite book beside the loo

(actually *Sodome et Gomorrhe*)
in your pied-à-terre

at the top of your parents' house.
Your father pronounced

your reading habits squalid.
Great art had been sullied.

(*Ulysses* must have been unreadable:
Bloom 'calm above his own rising smell'.)

You preferred long books:
you'd read *The Faerie Queene* twice.

Sir Charles Grandison, Clarissa,
Tristram Shandy, Chapman's Homer:

you liked them all
but Proust was special.

You never stopped reading Proust.
Marcel in love with someone he disliked.

*   *   *   *

Trinity lawn, effervescent with hailstones,
green eyes, high cheekbones,

wet, your dark brown fine hair
seeded, melting and molecular.

*   *   *   *

Your first poems were brilliant.
Unhappiness fired your talent.

That and the example of Sylvia Plath.
What happened? You doubted their worth.

Became hermetic. Nothing was published
and the impulse fastidiously vanished.

Thirty years later,
there are images I remember:

'a tongue of gravel',
parched, coming out of a cave;

Somerville library, 'old
spines buttered with gold';

sheep's wool snagged on barbed wire
'like the rare, precious hair

of the dead',
written when your father died.

*   *   *   *

Your first goldfish at Crick Road
vamped in Isadora Duncan mode,

a faintly corpulent Salome,
swathed in chiffon. It was 1970.

Her replacement wore organza,
was slimmer, harder, a fan dancer

in an orange fishtail dress.
Crick Road was a good address

in the right bit of north Oxford,
but you lived in a garden shed,

admittedly with diamond panes.
A dressmaker ran up some curtains.

You raided your father's stores
for porcelain, a 'T'ang' pottery horse,

you had beautiful stones in water
to deepen their colours.

You bought a hideous sofa bed
for us, a double, and hid

its horror under Mexican blankets.
The goldfish were decoration, thankless

inflections of interior design.
But, inside, things were going wrong.

C. S. Lewis's *Allegory of Love*
was somewhere on your shelves,

insisting on space
between the literal surface

and the underlying truth.
Something definitely stank of fish:

the soupçon of bouillabaisse
that last night's intercourse

had left in your cunt.
I wanted sexual excitement.

You wanted a labour of love
where push came to shove

and the clitoris led me a dance.
I felt like a dunce

trying to anticipate
your testy reprimands too late:

too hard, why did you move?
too soft, why don't you move?

What I was doing was quite difficult:
wanking while fucking, braces and belt.

Not from behind. One of your quirks.
But it usually eventually worked.

Your favourite sexual fantasies
were colours and green fields.

It took a week of talk before
you would wear a see-through bra

in bed. A 'scenario' never repeated.
Somehow it felt a bit stilted.

You kept your PrettyPolly hold-ups on
once and I came too soon.

I wanted to experiment.
And if you wouldn't,

I'd find someone who would.
By accident. Not in cold blood.

It wouldn't be my fault.
Then you thought you were going bald.

Counting the hairs. Every morning,
the brush inspection.

In Blackwell's, you saw a new book on Pater
and Arnold, by David Delaura.

You phoned. You'd wept all day.
You came and wept in the V & A –

in case your ideas were in his book.
I advised you to buy, to take a look.

In Strasbourg, the previous year,
I'd startled a rooted fear.

I'd fucked you half dressed,
wearing a leather vest,

and with your knickers on,
cutting into your arsehole and cunt.

At the Musée de l'oeuvre Notre-Dame next day,
we saw Grünewald's *Les amants trépassés*:

rents in the skin,
blowflies sipping a chancred shin,

riddled with snakes, worm-casts,
earthworms with waterproof elastoplasts,

a toad at her hairless twat.
I wanted the postcard.

You said you felt sick.
Your face was in shock.

When I left, you went through my letters,
burning out filth with your cigarette.

*   *   *   *

Everything goes, everything goes,
except for you cross-legged in bedclothes,

turning to rumple my hair,
then starting to put on your bra

the way that you put on your bra
(circular stitched from British Home Stores)

not both hands blindly behind,
but fastening the catch in front,

turning it round, hauling it up,
and squeezing each arm through its strap.

This simple ceremony lives
for as long as I am alive.

*   *   *   *

In Strasbourg, when I visited you,
you introduced me to couscous,

choucroute, priorité à droite.
You were very affectionate.

At the station, you took off my specs
and kissed me all over my face.

I was your 'Wizzledy Man'
and you were pleased to see me again.

We ate a quiche, a quiche Lorraine.
Quiche hadn't reached England then.

I'd borrowed a tent,
though we had to spend

one night in a proper hotel.
So you could dispel

your mother's suspicions.
One night was a sop to your conscience.

With hotels, your mother assumed
it would be separate rooms.

I'd bought a pair of sleeping bags
that zipped together. The latest trick.

Easter. But cold under canvas. It snowed.
The temperature fell below zero.

We listened to the forecast
on your portable before breakfast.

Stuttgart, Frankfurt: *minus zwei*.
München: *minus* fucking *drei*.

Except for us, the little campsite
was completely deserted,

neat and clean with snow.
There was a pale-grey sentry-go

of our footprints
to the camp latrines.

We fucked, then put on our clothes
to sleep in a frozen doze.

We walked to the village and mooned
over the caravan showroom.

In Munich, we saw *Carmen*
and I understood what opera meant

for the very first time.
The singing held me in its arms.

We saw Fellini's *Satyricon*
and *The Reivers* with Steve McQueen.

Halfway through eating *Linzertorte*, say,
in the Residenz café,

or after ten minutes in the Pinakothek,
I'd feel the snow-melt down my neck.

So we bought me a poet's black hat.
I tried a phrase: *das passt mir gut.*

My German was better than yours.
At a distance of thirty years,

we seem close, you and I,
we are almost certainly happy.

Happy without knowing why.
(As, later, unhappy without knowing why.)

Now the reason seems obvious:
we were close because we were close.

We were on top of each other.
The only time we really lived together.

Together and completely on our own.
There were no lodgers, no separate rooms.

My feet must have stunk.
I was using some cortisone junk

for eczema, when what
I had was athlete's foot.

All night in my sleep,
I'd itch my weeping insteps

through my socks.
You were the soul of tact

when I apologised in the morning.
Much better than snoring.

You told me you were awake already
with a sort of nervous malady

which started at boarding school:
except it wasn't your arsehole,

you said you were the same
as Le Pétomane,

and once your cunt started
you couldn't stop farting.

I licked a nostril, kissed your chin.
Never so close again.

An ex-prisoner-of-war
(who pronounced Manchester

as if he were born in Moss Side)
was in charge of the site.

He gave us apples from his store
and, when we left, one apple more

to plant in English ground:
ein Apfel in der Erde macht viele Bäume.

I visualise the apple now:
white stone broken brown

ulcerated flesh
deliquescent slush

ebony seeds
softening to suede

*   *   *   *

Early days. I don't remember when.
Caruso singing on Supraphon.

Something light and popular.
'Vieni sul mar'.

A slightly breathless,
deliberate band. (In the brass,

a moustached player
with a naked tuba

on his lap,
giving her a kiss on the lips . . .)

What's wrong? Why?
I'd seen your heartbroken eyes.

It's nothing, you said.
Just that Caruso died.

*   *   *

For breakfast you ate
chocolate fingers, *langues de chat*,

waffles with maple syrup,
Chamonix biscuits, doughnuts,

or Petit Suisse
with sugar. Anything sweet.

*   *   *

Food. At Stoneleigh, Watlington,
one of your lodgers, Michael Western,

was a brilliant cook.
Eels with prunes, chocolate cake,

for 50p each.
A quid for a really memorable lunch,

like Michael's moussaka
or his pukkha

Elizabeth David coq au vin,
where you paid extra for wine.

You made me give Michael the sack
for blotting his copybook

the first evening he arrived
with a throbbing car on the drive.

He'd thrown his suitcase and holdall
on the landlord's walnut table

and didn't seem to care about the scratch.
Loud music. Louder smell of hash.

When you started to scratch your face,
I agreed to give him notice.

Blood, snot and tears.
Full-blown hysteria.

So he got a month's notice to leave.
And stayed the full month before he moved.

Cooking prawns with wild rice.
Being there. Being nice.

*　*　*　*

What else do I remember?
Your chrome tea-infuser,

the combination of your cycle lock,
the number of the beast, 6 6 6,

your arsehole's iodines,
hairs like an icon's

calibrated nimbus,
your black smoking bush,

the dark brown lips
labyrinthine as a molten iris.

The most beautiful I've ever seen.
The most beautiful that's ever been.

*　*　*　*

You pronounced 'barely'
as if it were 'barley'.

I once said to Tim Hilton,
why are you working on Ruskin?

And Tim was furious.
I know the man who made his truss.

I borrowed your teeth for Judina
and gave your cunt to Ivinskaya.

Disjecta membra scattered everywhere,
unrecognisable, through my oeuvre:

complex, trivial, true.
And now I have re-membered you.

You difficult, lovely, lost masterpiece,
this is my purpose.

To make you real.
To make you see, to make you feel,

to make you hear.

To make you here.